Essential Fiction
Anthology

COMPILED BY

Brian Moses

Heinemann

Contents

Not Always a Perfect Place

Judy Waite

1901

I've been out today, standing in the crowds trying to catch a glimpse of Queen Victoria's funeral procession. Everyone said I was mad to go at my grand old age, but she's been a good Queen and I wanted to pay my last respects.

I couldn't see much at first – there were so many people – but then a smartly dressed elderly gentleman helped me to the front. I turned to thank him, and as his eyes met mine I saw something wonderful – something I've been waiting over sixty years to see.

10   Let me explain how it all started.

1837

My cousin Beatrice and I had gone out to watch Queen Victoria's coronation procession. There were crowds that day too, everyone jostling and shoving, all trying to get a better view. I got knocked several times, and Beatrice was cross because her new silk dress was getting crushed.

'I cannot abide this crowd,' grumbled Beatrice as a rough-looking man elbowed his way past her. 'Do let us go home. I hate all this shoving.'

I nodded. 'We'll see better from your balcony anyway.
20   It's busier down here than we thought it would be.'

We hurried back to where Beatrice lived. It wasn't far. It was one of the grand new houses they'd built along the edge of the park.

As we reached her gate Beatrice suddenly gripped my arm and pointed at something huddled up in the garden, 'Whatever is that?'

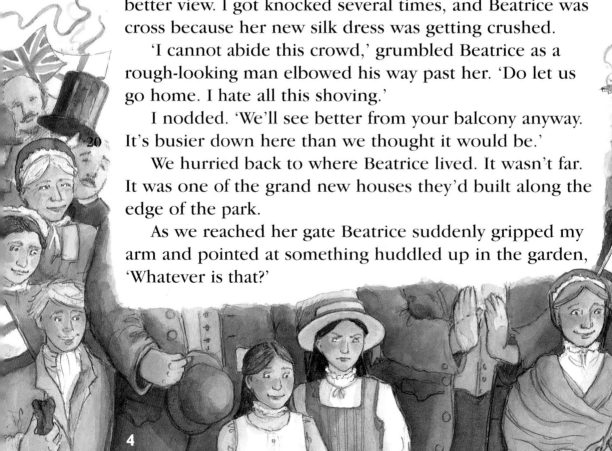

4

I peered over to where she was pointing. It looked like a pile of old rags.

'It's moving,' Beatrice whispered.

30   Then I realised what it was. It was a boy scrambling to his feet. I'd seen poor people before, of course, but never so thin. Never so dirty. And never so near.

He stepped back, shielding his face with his hands.

'Don't hit me. I ain't done nothing.'

'We're not going to hurt you, I promise,' I said.

Beatrice made a grab at my arm, 'Come away, Olivia. He's crawling with lice. He's probably got cholera too.'

I ignored her and stepped nearer the boy. Beatrice was right. He was filthy and he smelt disgusting, but the thing 40 that really drew my eye was a cut across his cheek. It was very deep, and in the shape of a cross, like an ugly red kiss on the side of his face.

'What happened?' I asked. 'Who hurt you like this?'

The boy coughed, and the harsh sound seemed to rip through his whole body, 'Old Soames, the overseer at the match factory where I work. He got the belt out and whipped me this morning.'

Beatrice interrupted him, 'He must have had a reason for beating you.'

50   He turned to look at her. 'He hit me because I fell, miss. Old Soames doesn't like anyone fainting, or getting sick. But the factory fumes get in my throat and in my chest, and make me feel dizzy and sick.' He coughed again. 'Please don't tell anyone about me. I'll never go back to that factory. I'll find other work. I'll work hard, and I'll make a better life for myself somehow.'

'Send him away,' Beatrice whispered to me. 'Give him a chance to go. He must be crawling with fleas. The maid will have to wash the path down once he's gone.'

60   'But it seems so cruel not to help him,' I whispered back. I turned again to the boy. 'How old are you?'

The boy shrugged. 'Don't know. I can't count numbers and things.'

Beatrice sniffed in disgust, 'Then you should go to school and learn.'

'Schools cost money. We ain't got none.'

'Well you were fortunate to have a job in the factory. People like you don't know when you're well off.'

'Don't be so heartless, Beatrice,' I said. 'Does that man
70 beat you often?' I asked the boy.

'Not much.' He gave a hollow laugh. 'Only if we cough. If we sneeze. If we cry.'

Suddenly we heard footsteps and a shadow fell across the path. 'So there you are, you wretched boy!'

I recognised the man straight away. It was the one who'd pushed past Beatrice in the crowd earlier.

The boy recognised him too. 'It's Mr Soames,' he said. 'From the factory.' He looked around wildly for some way to escape.

80 Soames pushed through the gate and I tried to block the path.

'Keep away,' I cried. 'You've no right to come in here.'

'Get out of my way,' he growled.

'Don't let him get me.' The boy's voice was pleading. 'Last week he hung a girl upside down from the ceiling because she'd run away. She hung there all day.'

Even Beatrice looked shocked, 'Do children sometimes die there?'

'All the time, miss. They die of coughing. They die of
90 beatings. They die of being caught up in machines. And sometimes they die because they're too tired to stay alive any more.'

I felt a rush of anger and turned to the man. 'You should take more care over your apprentices. Surely if you looked after them better they'd be stronger and fitter? It would be better for all of you.'

Soames gave a short laugh, 'I've done a lot worse than he's ever had to do. At his age I was working down in the

sewers. The smell in there rots your nostrils away. It's cold and it's dark. Some nights I was attacked by rats as big as dogs. Look!' He rolled his sleeve up to show long ugly scars running down his arm.

Beatrice pulled a face. 'That looks dreadful.'

'So it is, lady. But the world's not always a perfect place. We all have to live as best we can.'

I was feeling really miserable. There wasn't anything I could do to help the boy, but when I turned to look at him, he'd gone.

'Slipped away, the little eel. Sly as foxes they are. If I ever catch him, he'll pay for this, believe me!' muttered Soames. I watched as he hurried off down the street.

'Thank goodness they've gone,' Beatrice grabbed my arm. 'The crowd are really shouting now. I think the procession must be almost here.'

We ran together into Beatrice's house, up the huge staircase and out on to the balcony. We were just in time to see the beautiful coach with the new Queen in it pass by.

'Long live the Queen!' cried the crowd.

'Long live the Queen!' cried Beatrice.

'Long live the Queen!' I cried. But although I shouted and waved like everybody else, I kept thinking of the thin, ragged little boy who, from the looks of him, might not get the chance to live very long at all.

So that was it. The day of Queen Victoria's coronation. I've never forgotten it, but it hasn't been the beautiful coach and horses that have stayed in my head. It's the memory of that frightened, ragged little boy that has haunted me. I always hoped that he'd survived and managed to make a better life for himself after all.

And that was the wonderful thing that happened at the funeral procession today. As I turned to thank the smart elderly man who had so kindly helped me, I got a good look at his face. There was a big scar, shaped like a kiss, across his left cheek.

Illustrated by Rhianon Powell

7

Raiders!

LYNNE BENTON

When Jack Watson sleeps in an old tent in the garden he goes through a time-slip and finds himself back in the time of the Viking raids. His name is Edric and he and his sister Elfreda are the children of a brave Saxon chief.

As soon as I was inside the tent, I lay down and closed my eyes.

It is cool, dark and silent. No birds are singing. It is early dawn and I am on my way to the riverbank looking for firewood. I should have collected it yesterday, but I forgot. When I reach the high ground, overlooking the river, I look down.

Then I freeze.

A long, narrow boat, with a dragon's head at the front, is gliding silently along. There are round metal things hanging over the sides, and I realise they are shields. The oars dip in and out of the water without a sound. My mouth goes dry. I am almost too terrified to move, but some instinct warns me to drop to my stomach, out of sight. I crawl to the edge and watch.

The boat pulls up by the bank. It is full of huge men, with long fair hair underneath iron helmets.

Raiders!

They are quiet, intent and menacing. I have never seen so many men make so little noise.

With hardly a sound, they spill out of the boat, lifting off their round shields to take with them. They are all carrying axes and swords. They look like giants. Then they begin to creep purposefully towards the village. My village, where Father and Mother and Elfreda are asleep.

And I remember what the stranger told us about the terrible things the raiders had done in his village. I am horribly afraid.

8

30   I reach for my wooden swallow. I need it now, to
bring me luck.

      It is not there. I must have forgotten to pick it up.
It must be in the hut. I try not to think of this as an ill
omen.

      Trying desperately to keep out of sight, I wriggle
backwards until I cannot see the raiders any more. Then
I leap to my feet and start to run, faster than I have ever
run in my life. My feet skim over the rough grass.

My heart is pounding, and I am terrified, but I dare
not stop. I have to warn them. Only when I reach the
fence do I dare to look over my shoulder. The raiders are
not in sight yet, but I know they cannot be far behind. I
run inside and bar the gate. Then I race to the nearest
hut and bang on the door.

'Raiders!' I shout. 'Help! Raiders! Help!'

I don't wait for an answer, but run to the next hut.
'Raiders!'

I can hear people stirring behind me as I race through
the village. I cannot stop until I have warned Father.

Suddenly I hear a loud splintering noise behind me
as the raiders attack the gate with their axes. Then they
surge into the village, with terrible, bloodcurdling cries.

As I reach our hut, the door opens and Father comes
out brandishing his sword.

'Well done, Edric,' he cries. 'We're ready for them!'

Then I realise everyone is awake. There is a lot of
shouting and the clash of swords and spears. We Anglo-
Saxons may not be as big as them, but we are fierce when
we're threatened. We won't give in without a fight.

'Look after your mother and sister, Edric,' calls Father
as he charges into the battle. The noise is deafening now.
I turn and see the other women and children huddled at
the fence, away from the fighting.

Mother and Elfreda are in the hut. Mother is looking
desperately worried, but Elfreda's eyes are sparkling with
excitement. 'I want to join in!' she says.

'Oh, Elfreda!' I say, exasperated, as I hurry them out of
the hut.

Then Elfreda sees what is happening, and hears all the
shouting and the fearful clashing of weapons. She picks
up a stout stick and as we reach the others she says
bravely, 'Don't worry about us, Edric. I'll look after
Mother and the other children.' And I know she won't
give in without a fight, either.

'I must go and help Father!' I cry, and hurry off to find him.

There are men fighting everywhere, but I can't see Father. Then a huge hand is clamped over my mouth. I struggle and find myself in the grip of an enormous
80 raider. He is incredibly strong and I am paralysed with terror. I cannot even scream.

And suddenly Father is here. His sword is battered and has smears of blood on it. I have never seen him look so fierce. 'Leave my son alone!' he bellows, charging at the man.

With a roar, the raider pushes me aside and turns to Father. He has a heavy axe in his hand. He whirls it round his head. The axe cuts the sword in two, as if it was no more than a twig. Father is left holding the stump as the
90 Viking lifts his axe again.

'Father!' I scream. 'Look out!'

Father dodges as the axe falls where his head would have been. But the axe has caught his shoulder, and I see blood spurt out from the deep wound. His sword arm dangles, useless. I must help him. What can I do?

Then I remember my lucky swallow, still in the hut. It is my last hope. But as I turn, I see our roof is now alight. I must hurry.

I dive in, snatch up my swallow from the bench, when
100 I see the raider raise his axe again.

I am so angry I don't stop to think. I stand in the doorway and fling the wooden swallow at him with all my might. To my great satisfaction, it hits him on the forehead. Startled, he staggers back and drops the axe. Father grabs it.

'Well done, Edric!' he says, glancing over his shoulder at me. Then his eyes widen with horror.

'The roof!' he cries. 'Look out!'

But before I can move, everything goes black.

Illustrated by Peter Sutton and Tony Morris

A Jumble for the Queen

JULIA DONALDSON

Narrator
Percival Platter – *a pastry cook in Sir Richard Ash's house*
Joan – *a maid, aged twelve*
Tom – *Joan's schoolboy brother, aged ten*
Tom's schoolmaster
Queen Elizabeth I

Scene 1

Narrator   *It's seven of the clock and a fine summer morning.*

Percival   Too fine! I'm sweating already. And I can't find the minced dates.

Narrator   *In Sir Richard Ash's house in Kent everyone is busy: the serving men and the stable lads, the butlers and the brewers, the carvers and the chambermaids …*

Percival   And the cooks!

Narrator   *How many cooks?*

Percival   I'm too busy to count. But not enough pastry cooks. Joan! Joan! Where is that little lie-a-bed?

Joan   I'm not lying in bed! I'm here and I'm cutting herbs.

Percival   Cutting herbs! What about the custard tarts? Don't you know the Queen comes here tonight?

10

Joan	Yes, Mr Platter. How could I not know? But the mistress said she needed some more herbs to strew on the floor. She said the Queen likes the smell of them.
Percival	The Queen likes the taste of custard tarts, that's all I care about, and she won't be getting any at this rate. Now, run along to the dairy and fetch some more milk.
Joan	Yes, sir.
Percival	Where did I put those minced dates? We'll never be ready in time!

Scene 2

Narrator	*Seven-fifteen of the clock, and Joan's brother Tom is late for school.*
Master	And where is your cap, Thomas?
Tom	It … it blew away, sir!
Master	I could beat you for being late, Thomas, and I could beat you for losing your cap. Do you want to be beaten?
Tom	No, sir.
Master	What is that on your satchel, Thomas?
Tom	Nothing, sir.
Master	Yes it is, it's your cap, and it's wet. Why is it wet, Thomas?
Tom	I … I was catching frogs in it on the way to school, sir.
Master	I think perhaps you do want to be beaten after all, Thomas.

Scene 3

Narrator *Ten of the clock, and the Queen is leaving London. Not just the Queen. Hundreds of people and thousands of horses. Wagons full of clothes and jewels, pictures, books, bedclothes …*

Queen And beer. Weak beer. Of all things, I detest strong beer.

Narrator *The people of London throng the streets to watch the magnificent procession pass by.*

50 **Everyone** Long live the Queen!

Queen I thank you, good people of London. I am leaving you now for the fair county of Kent. But though I am away, may your love for me remain in your hearts till I return.

Everyone God bless the Queen!

Scene 4

Narrator *Half-past ten of the clock. In Sir Richard's kitchen, the custard tarts are all made.*

60 **Percival** But not the quince pies! Joan! Joan! What are you doing with the vinegar? You should be peeling quinces.

Joan But the mistress asked me to make some tooth soap first.

Percival Tooth soap! Tooth soap! What do we want with tooth soap at a time like this?

Joan The mistress thought the Queen might need some for her teeth after eating all our puddings.

Percival She can't eat the puddings if we haven't
70 finished making them!

Joan It won't be long, sir. I've mixed the vinegar and
white wine. I just need to add the honey and then
boil it up.

Percival But what about the quince pies?
We'll never be ready in time!

Scene 5

Narrator *Eleven of the clock, and the
schoolboys are having their dinner.*

Master Thomas, don't cut your nails at the table!

Tom I'm sorry, sir.

80 **Master** What is the proper use of a penknife, Thomas?

Tom For shaping quills into pens, sir.

Master And how do you say in Latin, 'The boy who cuts his
nails with a penknife will be beaten'?

Tom Er … 'puer', that's 'the boy'. 'Puer …' I don't know
the rest, sir.

Master And you didn't know your Latin poem this
morning. Latin is the key to all knowledge,
Thomas, haven't I told you that?

Tom Yes, you have, sir.

90 **Master** I have told you in words, Thomas,
but now I think that perhaps the
birch rod will speak to you better
than I can. You will bring me the
rod after dinner, Thomas.

Tom Oh no, sir, please, sir, no!

Master Oh yes, Thomas!

Illustrated by Nick Schon

The Stove Haunting

BEL MOONEY

*Daniel has gone through a time-slip and found himself back
in the last century in a time of terrible poverty and unrest.
Although his own circumstances are good, he meets others
who are suffering badly …*

At the end of the path was a tiny house, this one truly
like a hut. The walls seemed to be made of dirt or clay,
and they gaped with holes. The thatched roof dropped
down to the ground on each side like dirty hair round a
poor and grubby face. There were holes in the thatch
too, and the two small windows on each side of the door
were stuffed with sacking. In the pale light of the moon
the little building looked bleak and cold. And all the time
the desperate crying went on, coming from within.

10   The door opened as soon as George knocked, and a
man clasped him warmly by the hand. He nodded down
at Daniel and drew them both inside, leading them
across to two rough wooden boxes that served for chairs
on each side of the fire.

'Will you take a drop of beer, George?' the man asked.
He looked relieved when George shook his head and his
hunched shoulders relaxed a little.

The cottage consisted of one small room, lit by two
candles. An iron pot was hanging by a black chain over
20   the open fire. The floor was trodden earth but two dirty
sacks had been laid in front of the fire as a makeshift
carpet. On a shelf in the wall by the fire stood two
onions, placed as if they were precious objects. On the
rough wooden table, which was the only proper furniture
in the room, together with the bench which stood by it,
was half a loaf of dark grainy bread and an earthenware
pot with a knife stuck in it. The man pointed to these.
'So, will you take a bit o' bread and lard?' he asked.
George shook his head again.

30   In one corner of the room, just where the tiny staircase curled up behind the fire, a woman sat on a pile of sacks on the floor. In her arms was a child of about eighteen months, and it was still crying. Neither parent seemed to notice the sound. It was as if they had grown so used to it that they did not bother to make hushing sounds, or even to rock the baby any more. The mother raised exhausted eyes to the visitors, tried to smile, but failed.

    'I hope you're well, George?' she managed to whisper
40 at last, as if it were almost too much of an effort to speak.

    'How's the little 'un?' he asked instead of replying.

    The mother seemed to shrink back on the sacks, and now made pathetic rocking movements with her bony arms.

    'Bad, George, there's a fever now and he's been coughing as if his little chest would break in two.'

    'And the others?' asked George.

    'Not so bad, thanks be. Young William's started work now, and Rose went out
50 stone-picking with the gang; and the twins done well with the lazin'.'
She pointed proudly to the small sack of flour, made from the grains of wheat the family had managed to pick up after harvest, to make their bread with during the long winter.

'Do you go up and see 'em, lad?' said the man to Daniel, making him jump. ''Tis not often we have visitors here.' George nodded his head in the direction of the flight of stairs, so Daniel had no choice. He started to climb the narrow, twisting stairway, and to his relief George followed him up.

The stairs led straight into the single room which formed the top floor of the cottage. By the light of a single candle, Daniel could see that the room was crammed with beds. An old piece of material, like a ragged sheet, had been hung across the centre of the room in an attempt to divide it in two. On one side was a wide bed, covered with rough, woollen blankets, and with a home-made wooden cradle at its foot. On the other side was one small bed and a rough shelf-like structure against the wall, serving as another bed. These two had sacks instead of blankets, and held four children, who peered at Daniel. The oldest, a girl, lay on the hard shelf-bed, head bent over a scrap of sewing in her hand.

The three boys shared the single bed: one scraped away at a stick with a sharpened stone, and the other two, twins with shocks of red hair, lay quietly, not asleep, but watching their brother and sister. None of them smiled at the visitors, although the oldest boy, William, nodded shyly at them. The girl looked sullen and beaten; all of them were terribly thin. Their arms were like sticks poking out from the coarse smocks they wore, even in bed.

George greeted them, but expected no reply. It was as if these children could not speak. With the exposed, damp thatch above their heads, the piles of grubby sacks covering them, and their white pinched faces, Rose, William and the twins looked pitiful. Daniel wanted to turn away.

'All right?' he mumbled, and William made a dull, flat sound like 'Ah', as if he had no choice but to agree.

'As right as can be expected,' said George sadly, behind Daniel's back.

Downstairs again George laid a sympathetic hand on the man's shoulder.

'Well, William, you've good children there.' He nodded. The baby had stopped crying now and George glanced across to where it lay peacefully in its mother's arms.

'See that, Dan? Quiet at last. You know why the child's been crying so?'

Daniel shook his head. He felt a cold draught cut keenly through the holes in the walls, so that the low fire brightened for a moment and the candles flickered. George was looking at him intently.

'Because he's sick, lad! Seven of them, sleeping up there in that room, and at night the rain comes in through the roof, and dirt and vermin fall on the baby's head. When the weather's really bad, the drain water runs into this room here! Sick, that baby, and no wonder! And, do you know what Mr Winterton said when William asked him for some milk for the baby? He said it was for to fatten up his pigs, so's he couldn't spare it. *Pigs*, Daniel!'

Illustrated by Gary Long

Family Photo Album

That's me:
in the hospital with my mum –
Only two hours old –
even then I sucked my thumb

And here's me again:
I think I was nearly three
Look – I had a comfort sheet
it went everywhere with me

And that's Mum by our old car:
when she passed her driving test
Dad said 'It's a miracle –
anything could happen next!'

There's Mum and Dad in fancy dress:
it was Christmas '92
Mum said 'Go as a tramp, Dad –
and wear what you normally do!'

Oh, and here's Dad:
that day he built the wall
But Mum reversed into it
Dad wasn't pleased at all

This is my brother Jake:
that time he broke his leg
And Dad wrote on the plaster:
'Here comes Jake the Peg'

Ah, here's Jake again:
on the beach down at Dover
We built a brilliant sandcastle –
but a donkey knocked it over

Now, this is Mum:
on the day that Mum and Dad met
It's Dad's favourite picture –
he's got it on his desk

And there's all of us:
a few Christmases ago
Jake pulled a funny face
Mum said you'd never know

And, oh that seems to be it –
I've nothing left to show
We don't take photos any more –
but you can watch our video

James Carter

Illustrated by Tony Ross

My Grandpa

My grandpa is as round-shouldered as a question-mark
And is led about all day by his walking stick,
With teeth that aren't real,
Hidden behind a moustache that is,
While his memories simmer warmly
inside his crinkled paper bag of a face.
My grandpa,
Old and worn on the outside,
Sparky and fresh on the in.
For he often,
Shakes my hand with fifty-pence pieces,
Makes sweets pop out from behind his ears,
Smokes all day like a train
Then laughs like one as well.
Plays jokes on my mother
as he tries to freshen her face with a smile,
And then tells me stories that electrify my brain.
But best of all,
When my dad loses his temper,
Grandpa just tells him
TO SIT DOWN AND BEHAVE HIMSELF.
Good old grandpa.

Ian Souter

Illustrated by Tony Ross

21

Something Told the Wild Geese

Something told the wild geese
    It was time to go,
Though the fields lay golden
    Something whispered, 'Snow!'
Leaves were green and stirring,
    Berries, lustre-glossed,
But beneath warm feathers
    Something cautioned, 'Frost!'

All the sagging orchards
    Steamed with amber spice,
But each wild breast stiffened
    At remembered ice.
Something told the wild geese
    It was time to fly —
Summer sun was on their wings,
    Winter in their cry.

RACHEL FIELD

Snow Spell

This is our summer place

But the trees are bare
and all the leaves are crisp
and the river that we paddled in
is slow and clinks with ice.
The air smokes from us
our voices echo thin and sharp as sleet
and everything is sleeping under snow.

In summer we were playing here,
we built a dam,
my skimmer bounced six times,
a wet dog ate our sandwiches
and Dad fell off the stepping stones,
you swam your first five strokes.
The air was full of barks and laughs and shouts

Not long ago, before the spell of snow.

BERLIE DOHERTY

Illustrated by Tom Saecker

Time Spinner

ROY APPS

Rosemary lives on a 21st century space colony, but believe it or not she's bored stiff and would love to go back in time to the 1990s!

It all started with the fishes' fingers.

I was alone in my BedCube. Lying on the bed with my eyes shut. Imagining I was alive in Elizabethan times; back in the 1990s. Bicycle-riding, skateboarding, swimming – it must have been great to have been an Elizabethan.

'Rosemary!' Mum's voice boomed from the corridor. 'We're off now!'

I don't know why she sounded so excited. Dad was only taking her to the Wilkinses at number 4023 for a SupaDisk SoftWare Party. Yawn. Bore. All they do at these SoftWare parties is sit around and swap one old DigiTuneDisk for another even older DigiTuneDisk. They all sound the same anyway. Yawn. Bore.

I carried on imagining. This is what I imagined. I was bent over the steering handle of a bright red Elizabethan bicycle, racing hard down a steep, steep hill. Trees and buildings flashed past me in a whirl of colour and the wind whined and whistled through my ears.

'Have you gone deaf or something?' Mum was standing over me. Hands on hips.

'Eh?'

'I've been calling you for the last five minutes.'

Now Dad was on the scene.

'She spends too much time lying around moping, if you ask me,' he said.

I didn't ask you, I thought.

'I don't mope,' I said.

'Well, I don't know what else you'd call it.'

I don't suppose you would, I thought.

'Imagining has no useful function for anyone.
You're old enough to know that by now.'

Why does everything have to be *useful*? I thought.

'We won't be late back, love.' Mum's turn.

'Oh …?'

She gave me one of her quizzical looks. Did I sound
too disappointed? Did she suspect what I had in mind?

'What homework have you got tonight?'

'Elementary Astronomy and Technology.'

40   'Now, you *will* finish it before going to bed?'

'Of course, Mum.' My eyes smiled sweetly, but my fingers were tightly crossed behind my back; something Gran had taught me to do.

Elementary Astronomy and Technology are the last things you would *choose* to do if you were alone in the Domestic Living Unit with Gran. Because those times are brilliant times. Listening to Gran talk about the olden days is like having a busy picture painted for you in front of your very eyes. It's the only thing in the whole of the wide universe that's better than imagining.

'Bye!'

I lay back on my bed and looked around. Welcome to my BedCube. Yawn. Bore. A curved white ceiling reflects a pool of gentle light all around. All the furniture is moulded in pastel laminates: a pale pink dressing-table, soft green bed and chairs, grey VDU, grey TeleSatScreen. Yawn. Bore.

'What are you complaining about?' That's what Dad always says: 'It's clean and it's spacious and it's warm and it's comfortable …'

And it's just like *their* BedCube.

And it's just like Gran's BedCube.

It's just like every other cube in our Domestic Living Unit and every other Domestic Living Unit on the European Space Colony (Taurus IV).

And probably just like every Domestic Living Unit on Aquarius and Pisces, too. Not that I've ever been there.

I heard the hiss of the Domestic Living Unit door closing as Mum and Dad left for the Wilkinses. I listened, then counted to five, then listened again. All was quiet. I sat up, swung my legs round and leapt off the bed.

I pushed the bright green button by my BedCube door. It swished open. It always does. Yawn. Bore. Nothing ever breaks down on the European Space Colony (Taurus IV). I padded across the walkway and pushed the bright green button outside Gran's BedCube door.

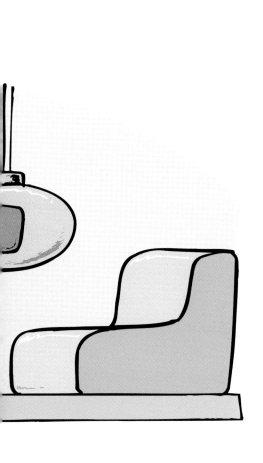

Illustrated by
Martin Chatterton

Metalmiss

LINDA PITT

Mr Grimshaw, the dreaded school inspector, has come to inspect Pinkerton Primary School. The inspector has already had a jug of water spilt on his suit when Mr Jones the headmaster introduces Metalmiss, the school's robot teacher!

Mr Grimshaw turned pale and shrank back against the wall as Metalmiss approached.

'Wha-wha-what's that?' he gasped.

Metalmiss gave him a cold stare.

'I am a robot teacher. Who are you?'

'Gr-Gr-Grimshaw.'

'Grimshaw?' Metalmiss paused. Her head swivelled towards Mr Jones. 'Is this the Grouchy Grimshaw who was mentioned in the staffroom, Mr Jones?'

10 'Well … yes … I mean … no …' stuttered Mr Jones helplessly as the school inspector glared at him.

'Is he to join my class?'

'Yes, in a way, but he's a …'

'Very well. Come into my classroom, Grouchy. And no more shouting.'

3R watched in amazement as a fat, bespectacled man was led into the room.

'We have a new pupil this afternoon, children. Grouchy Grimshaw.'

20 A giggle went round the classroom but was soon stopped by the robot's steely gaze.

'For the moment, Grouchy, you can sit there, in Rashid's place. He is away today.'

Mr Grimshaw sat down beside Harry.

'Now, Grouchy,' said Metalmiss, 'we have just completed some experiments with water. I will check that you are familiar with these. Harry, will you place the container of water in front of our new pupil?'

'Not water again!' groaned Mr Grimshaw.

30   'Pupils in 3R do not complain about their lessons, Grouchy. That is something you must learn. Now – when does water become solid?'

'When it freezes, of course,' said Mr Grimshaw scornfully.

'Good. Now I will make this water freeze.'

'I don't think you'll do that in a hurry,' laughed Mr Grimshaw, stirring the water with his finger. He wondered why he had ever felt frightened of this silly robot.

'Take your finger out,' hissed Harry.

'Remove your finger from the water, Grouchy,' ordered
40 Metalmiss.

'Why?' Mr Grimshaw stirred more wildly. 'Why should I?'

Metalmiss pointed at the water. The grey steel of her finger slowly changed to a brilliant, dazzling blue.

Harry grabbed Mr Grimshaw's hand and pulled it clear, just in time.

The water in the container was now a solid block of ice. Mr Grimshaw turned pale as he stared from his finger to the ice and back again.

'Is ice heavier or lighter than water, Grouchy?'

50 'Heavier,' said Mr Grimshaw faintly. He was still recovering from his chilling experience.

Holly raised her hand. 'It's lighter, Metalmiss, like an iceberg.'

'Good, Holly. That is correct.'

Harry began to feel sorry for Mr Grimshaw.

Metalmiss broke off a chunk of ice and they watched it float in a glass of water.

'I meant lighter,' growled Mr Grimshaw.

'Then you must say what you mean, Grouchy. But do not
60 worry. You will soon catch up with the other children in 3R.'

This was too much for Mr Grimshaw. He leapt to his feet.

'I am not a child!' he shouted. 'I will not be treated like a child!'

'Sit down at once, Grouchy.'

The robot's eyes were as cold as the ice in the glass. Mr Grimshaw sat down.

'You say that you are not a child. You are not a teacher. You are not a parent. What are you?'

'I am a School Inspector.'

70 'An inspector. I have not been programmed for that. Please wait.'

Metalmiss walked to the back of the room. Then she turned, pressed a small red button on the side of her left wrist, and pointed her left forefinger at the screen. Words beginning with 'I' slid rapidly across the screen and then halted.

'Here it is … "inspect" … "inspector" … "one who inspects; official employed to supervise a service and make reports".'

80 'That's it!' cried Mr Grimshaw triumphantly. 'I inspect schools and write reports. And what a report I'm going to write about this school!'

Metalmiss walked slowly back to the front of the classroom, turned round and stared at him.

'Will your report be a good one, Inspector?'

Mr Grimshaw's smile of triumph faded as his eyes met the robot's steely gaze.

'Er … yes,' he mumbled.

On the robot's cap a row of blue discs began to 90 revolve, slowly at first, then faster. The children nudged each other. They knew what was coming.

Even so, they gasped as the blue rays suddenly shot out and formed a halo above Mr Grimshaw's head.

'You are sure, Inspector?'

'Yes.'

The halo changed to purple, to grey, to black.

'It's a lie detector,' Harry whispered.

'You are still sure that it will be a good report?'

'No!' screamed Mr Grimshaw, knocking his chair over 100 as he jumped to his feet. 'I am going to write a VERY BAD REPORT!'

The halo disappeared.

'In fact,' Mr Grimshaw continued viciously, 'it will be the worst report that I have ever written. Sloppy school – sloppy teachers – and just wait until I tell Head Office about you, Metalmiss!'

'Sit down,' Metalmiss commanded.

110 For a moment Mr Grimshaw stared back defiantly. Then he shrugged, picked up his chair and sat down. He could wait.

Metalmiss turned to the class.

'And now, 3R, before you go to your music lesson I will read some more of our story.'

The story was about sailing ships and islands full of buried treasure. The robot's voice seemed softer, less metallic. On her tunic discs spun, glowed, changed colour.

As he listened, Mr Grimshaw removed his
120 glasses and began to breathe deeply. His face, usually so bad-tempered, grew softer, almost dreamy. He sat in a blur of colour, listening to the slow, clear voice. It was like a dream, he thought, the sort of dream that you want to go on for ever and ever.

The story ended. Quietly, the children went off to their music lesson. Mr Grimshaw sat on.

'Did you like our story, Inspector?'

Mr Grimshaw blinked, fumbled for his
130 glasses and put them on. He beamed at Metalmiss.

'It was wonderful – just wonderful. I can't find words to describe it.'

'But you will find words for your report, Inspector?'

'Yes, but now I will have to find new words, Metalmiss. It will be my first good report – a very good report.'

Illustrated by Martin Chatterton

The Tide Rises, the Tide Falls

The tide rises, the tide falls,
The twilight darkens, the curlew calls;
Along the sea-sands damp and brown
The traveller hastens toward the town,
And the tide rises, the tide falls.

Darkness settles on roof and walls,
But the sea, the sea in the darkness calls;
The little waves, with their soft white hands,
Efface the footprints in the sands,
And the tide rises, the tide falls.

The morning breaks; the steeds in their stalls
Stamp and neigh, as the ostler calls;
The day returns, but nevermore
Returns the traveller to the shore,
And the tide rises, the tide falls.

Henry Wadsworth Longfellow

Windy Nights

Whenever the moon and stars are set,
   Whenever the wind is high,
All night long in the dark and wet,
   A man goes riding by.
Late in the night when the fires are out,
Why does he gallop and gallop about?

Whenever the trees are crying aloud,
   And ships are tossed at sea,
By, on the highway, low and loud,
   By at the gallop goes he.
By at the gallop he goes, and then
By he comes back at the gallop again.

Robert Louis Stevenson

THE IRON MAN

TED HUGHES

The Iron Man came to the top of the cliff.

How far had he walked? Nobody knows. Where had he come from? Nobody knows. How was he made? Nobody knows.

Taller than a house, the Iron Man stood at the top of the cliff, on the very brink, in the darkness.

The wind sang through his iron fingers. His great iron head, shaped like a dustbin but as big as a bedroom, slowly turned to the right, slowly turned to the left. His iron ears turned, this way, that way. He was hearing the sea. His eyes, like headlamps, glowed white, then red, then infra-red, searching the sea. Never before had the Iron Man seen the sea.

He swayed in the strong wind that pressed against his back. He swayed forward, on the brink of the high cliff.

And his right foot, his enormous iron right foot, lifted – up, out, into space, and the Iron Man stepped forward, off the cliff, into nothingness.

CRRRAAAASSSSSH!

Down the cliff the Iron Man came toppling, head over heels.

CRASH! CRASH! CRASH!

From rock to rock, snag to snag, tumbling slowly. And as he crashed and crashed and crashed

His iron legs fell off.

His iron arms broke off, and the hands broke off the arms.

His great iron ears fell off and his eyes fell out.

His great iron head fell off.

All the separate pieces tumbled, scattered, crashing bumping, clanging, down on to the rocky beach far below.

34

A few rocks tumbled with him.

Then. Silence.

Only the sound of the sea, chewing away at the edge of the rocky beach, where the bits and pieces of the Iron Man lay scattered far and wide, silent and unmoving.

Only one of the iron hands, lying beside an old, sand-logged washed-up seaman's boot, waved its fingers for a minute, like a crab on its back. Then it lay still.

While the stars went on wheeling through the sky and the wind went on tugging at the grass on the cliff-top and the sea went on boiling and booming.

Nobody knew the Iron Man had fallen.

Night passed.

Just before dawn, as the darkness grew blue and the shapes of the rocks separated from each other, two seagulls flew crying over the rocks. They landed on a patch of sand. They had two chicks in a nest on the cliff. Now they were searching for food.

One of the seagulls flew up – Aaaaaark! He had seen something. He glided low over the sharp rocks. He landed and picked something up. Something shiny, round and hard. It was one of the Iron Man's eyes. He brought it back to his mate. They both looked at this strange thing. And the eye looked at them. It rolled from side to side, looking first at one gull, then at the other. The gulls, peeping at it, thought it was a strange kind of clam, peeping at them from its shell.

Then the other gull flew up, wheeled around and landed and picked something up. Some awkward, heavy thing. The gull flew low and slowly, dragging the heavy thing. This new thing had five legs. It moved. The gulls thought it was a strange kind of crab. They thought they had found a strange crab and a strange clam. They did not know they had found the Iron Man's eye and the Iron Man's right hand.

But as soon as the eye and the hand got together the eye looked at the hand. Its light glowed blue. The hand stood up on three fingers and its thumb, and craned its forefinger like a long nose. It felt around. It touched the eye. Gleefully it picked up the eye, and tucked it under its middle finger. The eye peered out, between the forefinger and thumb. Now the hand could see.

70

It looked around. Then it darted and jabbed one of the gulls with its stiffly held finger, then darted at the other and jabbed him. The two gulls flew up into the wind with a frightened cry.

Slowly then the hand crept over the stones, searching. It ran forward suddenly, grabbed something and tugged. But the thing was stuck between two rocks. The thing was one of the Iron Man's arms. At last the hand left the arm and went scuttling hither and thither among the rocks, till it stopped, and touched something gently. This thing was the other hand. This new hand stood up and hooked its finger round the little finger of the hand with the eye, and let itself be led. Now the two hands, the seeing one leading the blind one, walking on their finger-tips, went back together to the arm, and together they tugged it free. The hand with the eye fastened itself on to the wrist of the arm. The arm stood up and walked on its hand. The other hand clung on behind as before, and this strange trio went searching.

80

90

An eye! There it was, blinking at them speechlessly beside a black and white pebble. The seeing hand fitted the eye to the blind hand and now both hands could see. They went running among the rocks. Soon they found a leg. They jumped on top of the leg and the leg went hopping over the rocks with the arm swinging from the hand that clung to the top of the leg. The other hand clung on top of that hand. The two hands, with their eyes, guided the leg, twisting it this way and that, as a rider guides a horse.

Soon they found another leg and the other arm. Now each hand, with an eye under its palm and an arm dangling from its wrist, rode on a leg separately about the beach. Hop, hop, hop, they went, peering among the rocks. One found an ear and at the same moment the other found the giant torso. Then the busy hands fitted the legs to the torso, then they fitted the arms, each fitting the other, and the torso stood up with legs and arms but no head. It walked about the beach, holding its eyes up in its hands, searching for its lost head. At last, there was the head – eyeless, earless, nested in a heap of red seaweed. Now in no time the Iron Man had fitted his head back, and his eyes were in place, and everything in place except for one ear. He strode about the beach searching for his lost ear, as the sun rose over the sea and the day came.

120   The two gulls sat on their ledge, high on the cliff. They watched the immense man striding to and fro over the rocks below. Between them, on the nesting ledge, lay a great iron ear. The gulls could not eat it. The baby gulls could not eat it. There it lay on the high ledge.

Far below, the Iron Man searched.

At last he stopped, and looked at the sea. Was he thinking the sea had stolen his ear? Perhaps he was thinking the sea had come up, while he lay scattered, and had gone down again with his ear.

130   He walked towards the sea. He walked into the breakers, and there he stood for a while, the breakers bursting around his knees. Then he walked in deeper, deeper, deeper.

The gulls took off and glided down low over the great iron head that was now moving slowly out through the swell. The eyes blazed red, level with the wavetops, till a big wave covered them and foam spouted over the top of the head. The head still moved out under water. The eyes and the top of the head appeared for a moment in a

140   hollow of the swell. Now the eyes were green. Then the sea covered them and the head.

The gulls circled low over the line of bubbles that went on moving slowly out into the deep sea.

Illustrated by David Frankland

The Invisible Beast

The beast that is invisible
is stalking through the park,
but you cannot see it coming
though it isn't very dark.
Oh you know it's out there somewhere
though just why you cannot tell,
but although you cannot see it
it can see you very well.

You sense its frightful features
and its great ungainly form,
and you wish that you were home now
where it's cosy, safe and warm.
And you know it's coming closer
for you smell its awful smell,
and although you cannot see it
it can see you very well.

Oh your heart is beating faster,
beating louder than a drum,
for you hear its footsteps falling
and your body's frozen numb.
And you cannot scream for terror
and your fear you cannot quell,
for although you cannot see it
it can see you very well.

Jack Prelutsky

Illustrated by Emma Chichester Clark

Before the Hunt

Howling wind,
   hear me,
Dancing trees,
   hail me,
Cooling breeze,
   calm me,
Guiding sky,
   light my
way through the bush.
   As the stars
protect the lonely moon
   So may I
escape the snares
   in this living forest.
   As the cat
stalks its prey
   So may I
be first to spy my game.
   Living forest hear me
Chilling wind still my heart
Teasing shadows smile with me
Lead me to my hunt.

Lari Williams

Illustrated by Emma Chichester Clark

The Hobbit

J.R.R. TOLKIEN

*Bilbo, the Hobbit, is on a quest to raid the treasure
hoard of Smaug the dragon. Smaug releases his fury
on the nearby town.*

There was once more a tremendous excitement and
enthusiasm. But the grim-voiced fellow ran hotfoot to the
Master. 'The dragon is coming or I am a fool!' he cried.
'Cut the bridges! To arms! To arms!'

Then warning trumpets were suddenly sounded, and
echoed along the rocky shores. The cheering stopped
and the joy was turned to dread. So it was that the
dragon did not find them quite unprepared.

Before long, so great was his speed, they could see
him as a spark of fire rushing towards them and growing
ever huger and more bright, and not the most foolish
doubted that the prophecies had gone rather wrong. Still
they had a little time. Every vessel in the town was filled
with water, every warrior was armed, every arrow and
dart was ready, and the bridge to the land was thrown
down and destroyed, before the roar of Smaug's terrible
approach grew loud, and the lake rippled red as fire
beneath the awful beating of his wings.

Amid shrieks and wailing and the shouts of men he
came over them, swept towards the bridges and was
foiled! The bridge was gone, and his enemies were on an
island in deep water – too deep and dark and cool for his
liking. If he plunged into it, a vapour and a steam would
arise enough to cover all the land with a mist for days;
but the lake was mightier than he, it would quench him
before he could pass through.

Roaring he swept back over the town. A hail of dark
arrows leaped up and snapped and rattled on his scales
and jewels, and their shafts fell back kindled by his
breath burning and hissing into the lake. No fireworks
you ever imagined equalled the sights that night.

At the twanging of the bows and the shrilling of the trumpets the dragon's wrath blazed to its height, till he was blind and mad with it. No one had dared to give battle to him for many an age; nor would they have dared now, if it had not been for the grim-voiced man (Bard was his name), who ran to and fro cheering on the archers and urging the Master to order them to fight to the last arrow.

Fire leaped from the dragon's jaws. He circled for a while high in the air above them lighting all the lake; the trees by the shores shone like copper and like blood with leaping shadows of dense black at their feet. Then down he swooped straight through the arrow-storm, reckless in his rage, taking no heed to turn his scaly sides towards his foes, seeking only to set their town ablaze.

Fire leaped from thatched roofs and wooden beam-ends as he hurtled down and past and round again, though all had been drenched with water before he came. Once more water was flung by a hundred hands wherever a spark appeared. Back swirled the dragon. A sweep of his tail and the roof of the Great House crumbled and smashed down. Flames unquenchable sprang high into the night. Another swoop and another, and another house and then another sprang afire and fell; and still no arrow hindered Smaug or hurt him more than a fly from the marshes.

Already men were jumping into the water on every side. Women and children were being huddled into laden boats in the market-pool. Weapons were flung down. There was mourning and weeping, where but a little time ago the old songs of mirth to come had been sung about the dwarves. Now men cursed their names. The Master himself was turning to his great gilded boat, hoping to row away in the confusion and save himself. Soon all the town would be deserted and burned down to the surface of the lake.

That was the dragon's hope. They could all get into boats for all he cared. There he could have fine sport hunting them, or they could stop till they starved. Let them try to get to land and he would be ready. Soon he would set all the shoreland woods ablaze and wither every field and pasture. Just now he was enjoying the sport of town-baiting more than he had enjoyed anything for years.

But there was still a company of archers that held their ground among the burning houses. Their captain was Bard, grim-voiced and grim-faced, whose friends had accused him of prophesying floods and poisoned fish, though they knew his worth and courage. He was a descendant in long line of Girion, Lord of Dale, whose wife and child had escaped down the Running River from

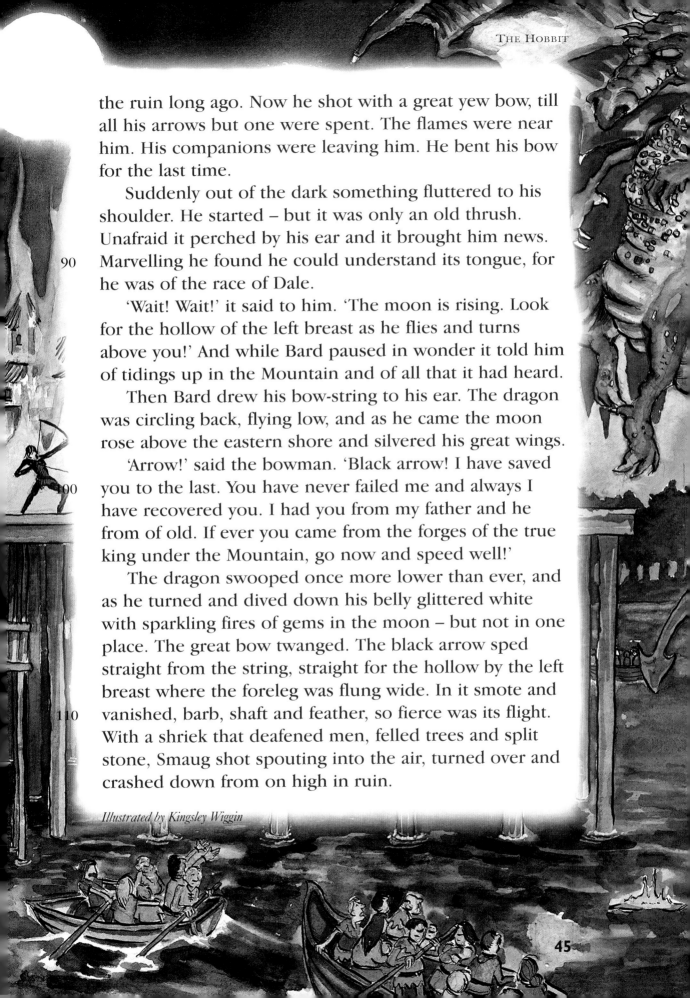

the ruin long ago. Now he shot with a great yew bow, till all his arrows but one were spent. The flames were near him. His companions were leaving him. He bent his bow for the last time.

Suddenly out of the dark something fluttered to his shoulder. He started – but it was only an old thrush. Unafraid it perched by his ear and it brought him news. Marvelling he found he could understand its tongue, for he was of the race of Dale.

'Wait! Wait!' it said to him. 'The moon is rising. Look for the hollow of the left breast as he flies and turns above you!' And while Bard paused in wonder it told him of tidings up in the Mountain and of all that it had heard.

Then Bard drew his bow-string to his ear. The dragon was circling back, flying low, and as he came the moon rose above the eastern shore and silvered his great wings.

'Arrow!' said the bowman. 'Black arrow! I have saved you to the last. You have never failed me and always I have recovered you. I had you from my father and he from of old. If ever you came from the forges of the true king under the Mountain, go now and speed well!'

The dragon swooped once more lower than ever, and as he turned and dived down his belly glittered white with sparkling fires of gems in the moon – but not in one place. The great bow twanged. The black arrow sped straight from the string, straight for the hollow by the left breast where the foreleg was flung wide. In it smote and vanished, barb, shaft and feather, so fierce was its flight. With a shriek that deafened men, felled trees and split stone, Smaug shot spouting into the air, turned over and crashed down from on high in ruin.

Illustrated by Kingsley Wiggin

Basia's Birthday Present

Robin Mellor

Note: Basia is a Polish name and should be pronounced 'Basha'

Basia pulled her thin, ragged coat closer over her shoulders. She listened to the cold wind as it howled around the ruined buildings where they had camped for a night's shelter. There were tears in her eyes. She wiped them away with the back of her hand. It was not just the cold wind that made her cry but the sadness of a child on a birthday, with no hope of having any presents.

'Basia!' Her mother called.

Basia turned away from the doorway and walked back into the yellow light of the little candle that flickered in the bare room.

'Basia,' said her mother. 'Why are you crying?'

'It's the wind, Mother,' Basia replied, but her mother knew what was making her daughter so unhappy.

'I'm sorry, Basia, but until we reach another land and find help we cannot afford any birthday presents. You know how hard it is to even find enough to eat. Come now, sit with Grandmother and have some soup.'

Basia sat next to her grandmother, who was wrapped for warmth in a great heap of blankets. She sipped the watery soup.

'You know,' said Grandmother, 'we are not the worst-off refugees. There's a family in the old building, across the way, and they've just had a new baby. Imagine, another mouth to feed.'

Basia thought to herself quietly. She should not be crying for a birthday present when there are people in greater difficulty than her. It was so sad for a new baby to have nothing for his birthday. Even the baby Jesus had some presents, and wasn't he like them, away from home in a strange place for the night?

After the candle had been blown out and everyone settled for the night, Basia tried to sleep. For a long time, she lay awake and when, at last, she drifted into a fitful sleep, she dreamed of a cold, lost baby, crying.

She awoke before dawn and, lying there with the cold nibbling at her hands and feet, she made up her mind that she must give the new baby a present.

It had snowed in the night and was still snowing, so her family decided to wait until the snow stopped before travelling on.

'After all,' said Mother, 'we might lose our way in the blizzard.'

Basia looked all around the ruined building for something that could be a birthday present for the baby. At midday, as she sat eating more thin soup, she looked at the small pile of things she had found. She had a small piece of sacking, some straw and a length of string. It was hopeless. How could she give a pile of rubbish as a present?

'What have you got those things for?' Grandmother asked.

'I want to give the new baby a present for his birthday, but this is all I could find.'

Grandmother hobbled across the room and turned the little pile over with her wrinkled hands. 'You could make a doll, Basia. Twist the string around the sacking and stuff it with the straw.'

Basia's fingers worked at the rough sacking and string. In a while she had fashioned it into a small figure. She did not have enough string for the top of the head so some of the straw was sticking out.

'It's all right, though,' she told Grandmother. 'It looks like hair. But there are no eyes. What use is a doll without eyes?'

Grandmother smiled and dipped her hand deep among the blankets she had wrapped around her.

'I knew they would come in useful.' she muttered, and pulled out two buttons. Basia tied them on to the doll's head and they gleamed in the cold daylight like real eyes.

Without waiting any longer Basia ran across to see the new baby. He was lying in his mother's arms. Both mother and child looked cold and hungry. The young woman looked up and smiled at Basia.

'Have you come to see my baby?' she asked.

'Yes,' said Basia. 'And I've brought him a present.'
She held out the doll.

'Oh, it's beautiful,' said the young mother. 'Thank you.'

When Basia returned, her grandmother looked up and asked, 'Well, was it all right?'

'Oh, yes,' said Basia, 'and I feel better now than I ever have. I feel as if I've had a birthday present myself.'

Grandmother put her arm around Basia's shoulder. 'Perhaps to give is better than to receive.'

Basia smiled. 'Perhaps,' she said. 'But I won't mind if I have a present next year.'

Illustrated by Rosalind Hudson

Diary of a Killer Cat

ANNE FINE

1. Monday

OKAY, OKAY. So hang me. I killed the bird. For pity's sake, I'm a *cat*. It's practically my *job* to go creeping round the garden after sweet little eensy-weensy birdy-pies that can hardly fly from one hedge to another. So what am I supposed to do when one of the poor feathery little flutterballs just about throws itself into my mouth? I mean, it practically landed on my paws: it could have *hurt* me.

Okay, *okay*. So I biffed it. Is that any reason for Ellie
10 to cry in my fur so hard I almost *drown*, and squeeze me so hard I almost *choke*?

'Oh, Tuffy!' she says, all sniffles and red eyes and piles of wet tissues. 'Oh, Tuffy. How could you *do* that?'

How could I *do* that? I'm a *cat*. How did I know there was going to be such a giant great fuss, with Ellie's mother rushing off to fetch sheets of old newspaper, and Ellie's father filling a bucket with soapy water?

Okay, *okay*. So maybe I shouldn't have dragged it in and left it on the carpet. And maybe the stains won't
20 come out, ever.

So *hang* me.

2. Tuesday

I QUITE ENJOYED the little funeral. I don't think they really wanted me to come, but, after all, it's just as much my garden as theirs. In fact, I spend a whole lot more time in it than they do. I'm the only one in the family who uses it properly.

Not that they're grateful. You ought to hear them.

'That cat is *ruining* my flower beds. There are hardly any of the petunias left.'

30 'I'd barely *planted* the lobelias before it was lying on top of them, squashing them flat.'

'I *do* wish it wouldn't dig holes in the anemones.'

Moan, moan, moan, moan. I don't know why they bother to keep a cat, since all they ever seem to do is complain.

All except Ellie. She was too busy being soppy about the bird. She put it in a box, and packed it round with cotton wool, and dug a little hole, and then we all stood round it while she said a few words, wishing the bird

40 luck in heaven.

'Go away,' Ellie's father hissed at me. (I find that man quite rude.) But I just flicked my tail at him. Gave him the blink. Who does he think he is? If I want to watch a little bird's funeral, I'll watch it. After all, I've known the bird longer than any of them have. I knew it when it was *alive*.

Illustrated by Tony Ross

Bill's New Frock

ANNE FINE

When Bill Simpson woke up on Monday morning, he found he was a girl.

He was still standing staring at himself in the mirror, quite baffled, when his mother swept in.

'Why don't you wear this pretty pink dress?' she said.

'I *never* wear dresses,' Bill burst out.

'I know,' his mother said. 'It's such a pity.'

And, to his astonishment, before he could even begin to argue, she had dropped the dress over his head and
10 zipped up the back. 'I'll leave you to do up the shell buttons,' she said. 'They're a bit fiddly and I'm late for work.'

And she swept out, leaving him staring in dismay at the mirror. In it, a girl with his curly red hair and wearing a pretty pink frock with fiddly shell buttons was staring back at him in equal dismay.

'This can't be true,' Bill Simpson said to himself. 'This cannot be true!'

He stepped out of his bedroom just as his father was
20 rushing past. He, too, was late in getting off to work. Mr Simpson leaned over and planted a kiss on Bill's cheek.

'Bye, Poppet,' he said, ruffling Bill's curls. 'You look very sweet today. It's not often we see you in a frock, is it?'

He ran down the stairs and out of the house so quickly he didn't see Bill's scowl, or hear what he muttered savagely under his breath.

Bella the cat didn't seem to notice any difference. She purred and rubbed her soft furry body around his ankles in exactly the same way as she always did.
30 And Bill found himself spooning up his cornflakes as usual. It was as if he couldn't help it. He left the house at the usual time, too. He didn't seem to have any choice.

Things, though odd, were just going on in their own way, as in a dream.

Or it could be a nightmare! For hanging about on the corner was the gang of boys from the other school. Bill recognised the one they called Mean Malcolm in his purple studded jacket.

I think I'll go round the long way instead, Bill thought to himself. I don't want to be tripped up in one of their nasty scuffles, like last week, when all the scabs were kicked off my ankle.

Then Bill heard the most piercing whistle. He looked around to see where the noise was coming from, then realised Mean Malcolm was whistling at him!

Bill Simpson blushed so pink that all his freckles disappeared. He felt so foolish he forgot to turn off at the next corner to go round the long way. He ended up walking right past the gang.

Mean Malcolm just sprawled against the railings, whistling at Bill as he went by wearing his pretty pink frock with shell buttons.

Bill Simpson thought to himself: I'd rather have the scabs kicked off my ankle!

When he reached the main road, there was an elderly woman with curly grey hair already standing at the kerb. To feel safe from the gang, he stood at her side.

'Give me your hand, little girl,' she said. 'I'll see us both safely across the road.'

'No, really,' insisted Bill. 'I'm fine, honestly. I cross here every day by myself.'

The woman simply didn't listen. She just reached down and grasped his wrist, hauling him after her across the road. On the far side, she looked down approvingly as she released him. 'That's such a pretty frock!' she said. 'You keep it nice and clean.'

Rather than say something disagreeable, Bill ran off quickly.

Illustrated by Martin Chatterton

Cheat!

JUDY WAITE

Danny has won first prize in a painting competition, but feels terrible because it is not his own work. He has taken old Mr King's painting and passed it off as his own.

He hadn't felt guilty – not even the next day, when Gran showed him the entry form in the local paper.

'I think we'll enter that painting of yours,' she said. She cut the form out, and handed Danny a pen. 'You made such a good effort. It just shows how well you can do, when you try.'

Danny filled in his name – his age – his address. All the evidence, neatly written for the world to see.

That same afternoon he went round with Gran to
10 deliver a meat pie to Mr King. Mr King's house felt warm and cheerful.

'Have you always been blind, Mr King?'

'*Danny*!' Gran's voice was shocked, but Mr King just smiled.

'Don't worry, Dora. He's just a lad.' He turned to Danny. Even though his eyes weren't looking at him, Mr King still somehow seemed to see him.

'I was about your age. My eyesight was never good, but as I got older, it grew worse. Things got more and
20 more blurry. And then, one day, I woke up and the world was completely black.'

'Weren't you scared?' It was so hard to imagine. Danny thought of all the things he would miss: football, telly, computer games. Poor Mr King. He could never be really free. Even his house was only safe as long as nothing moved.

'I suppose I learnt to make the best of it. But it upset my father more than anything. He was an artist – a good one too. Most of these pictures were his. And he'd had
30 hopes for me. I'd shown promise once …' The old man's voice trailed away, lost in distant memories.

54

Danny thought suddenly about the painting of the garden. He wished he could tell Mr King that he'd treasure it for ever. Maybe he'd find a way to tell him later. He couldn't say anything with Gran here.

He turned to ask another question, but Gran stepped in. 'That's enough, Danny! We really must be going. You're off home later today, and you've got packing to do!'

40   She got up and Danny followed, looking back just once. Mr King was smiling after them: that kind, gentle smile that lit up the blankness in his eyes.

It was the day of the presentation.

As Mum drove them to Blackport, Danny sat hunched in his seat. He kept hoping they would break down, or get stuck in an enormous traffic jam. Instead, the car zoomed along happily, and the road stayed clear.

They arrived with plenty of time to spare.

Danny saw the painting as soon as they walked into
50   the town hall.

It was hanging at the front of the room. A tag with the words FIRST PRIZE had been clipped to the bottom.

Mum tried to drag Danny towards it, but he pulled away. 'I've seen it before,' he muttered.

Mum squeezed his arm proudly. 'You shouldn't be so shy about it.'

Danny watched her hurry towards the painting. He wondered if there was still time to get out of the presentation. Perhaps he could pretend to faint. Perhaps he
60   could say he felt sick.

Mum came back, buzzing with excitement. 'It's brilliant. I never knew you had such a wonderful talent.'

Danny gave a groan of pain, and clutched his stomach. 'I don't feel very well.'

'I'm sure it's just nerves. You'll be fine once it all gets started.' Mum glanced up at the hall clock. 'We'd better go and sit down. The Mayor will be here soon.'

Danny trudged behind her. They squeezed in amongst the rows of chairs that were already filling up with
70 people. He couldn't even try out the 'fainting plan'. There wasn't enough room to fall over properly.

Mum nudged him suddenly, 'Look, Gran's here.'

Danny turned miserably towards the door. Gran was walking in, her arm linked with someone else. Danny hadn't known it was possible to feel any worse, but the 'rock' in his stomach hit a new low. The smiling, shuffling figure coming in with Gran was Mr King.

The buzz of voices died. The Mayor of Blackport strode importantly to the front and cleared his throat.
80 Danny didn't hear the speech. The presentations to the runner-up prize winners passed over him like a blur.

'And now, could we have our Young Artist of the Year – Danny Stokes …' The Mayor's voice seemed to boom and bounce through the hall.

Danny got up and made his way towards the front. He couldn't look at Mum. He couldn't look at Gran. He couldn't go through with it. Danny closed his eyes, and counted to ten. As he opened them slowly, he looked straight across at Mr King. Although Mr King couldn't see,
90 his eyes still shone with warmth and pride.

'Congratulations,' the Mayor said, smiling and shaking Danny's hand. 'It's a wonderful entry, a very worthy winner.'

Danny took the envelope. It felt bulky and exciting. He imagined the notes inside. Fifty pounds – it was loads of money. It could buy him a new computer game or maybe a football shirt, but he knew, deep down, that he'd never really enjoy them. They would never *really* be his.

He turned to face the audience. His voice was small,
100 croaky.

'I'm really pleased I won this. And … and I want to spend it on something really special.' As he paused, he felt a rush of feeling flood through him. He knew with certainty that he was doing the right thing.

Suddenly his voice became clear and strong. 'I've decided to give it to the Blind Association. I reckon they might need it more than I need a new computer game.'

For a moment there was a stunned silence. Then all at once the clapping started. The Mayor was squeezing his shoulder. People were rising to their feet. Through the swell of faces Danny could see Mum dabbing at her eyes with a hanky.

Everyone was cheering as he battled his way back to his seat. Strangers reached out to shake his hand or pat his back. Warm voices called out praises and congratulations. He was everybody's favourite. He was everybody's hero.

Mum hugged him tightly and Gran *almost* kissed him – although he managed to turn his head away just in time. It ended up as just a bit of slobber on his ear.

But the thing that really did it, the thing that made his heart do another crash landing, was Mr King.

The old man rose to his feet, stretching his fingertips to touch Danny's face. His eyes shone like lights. 'Not many lads would do that,' he said. 'You're even better than I first thought. You're something special, Danny. You're a really good lad.'

Danny stood, staring dumbly back at Mr King. It was all going wrong again – horribly wrong.

Danny didn't feel 'good' at all.

Illustrated by Beryl Sanders

Hiker's Haikus

This is the best way
To travel: on your two feet
Fuelled by bread and meat.

On footpaths, through fields
Of daisies, cowslips, clear streams,
Alone with your dreams.

Far from motorway's
Incessant roar, dust and stink –
Slow steps, time to think.

Inhaling pure air
Seasoned with birdsong, green scent
No one could invent.

Quiet happiness,
Moving thoughtful, calm and slow;
The best way to go.

Vernon Scannell

Illustrated by Gary Davies

Tomb Tunes

Here lies the body
Of a poor, tired Dad,
Driven by his children
Crazy, mad.

Here lies the body
Of a worn-out Mum,
Moaned at, overworked,
Ignored, glum.

Here lies the body
Of an only child,
Peevish, selfish,
Reckless, wild.

Here lies the body
Of a ten-year-old;
Didn't do
As he was told.

Here lie the bodies
Of family folk
Kind and loving –
Must be a joke!

John Kitching

Illustrated by Gary Davies

My Pet

My
Pet
Doesn't
Have
A
Tail
My
Pet's
Got
No
Legs
My
Pet
Doesn't
Fly
Or
Sing
My
Pet
Doesn't
Beg

My
Pet
Isn't
Furry
But
It's
One
You
Won't
Mistake
For
My
Pet
Is
A
Curly
Wurly
Hissy
Kissy
Long
And
Lovely ...

Tony Bradman

Illustrated by Gary Davies

A WHO'Z WHO OF THE 'HORRIBLE HOUSE'

Inside
the
'Horrible
House'
there is
an awful aquamarine apparition abseiling
a bug-eyed beige bogyman boxing
a cackling crimson cockroach creeping
a disgusting damson Dracula dancing
an eerie emerald elf electrocuting
a flopping flame Frankenstein fencing
a grotty green ghost groaning
a haunting hazel hag hammering
an insane indigo imp ice-screaming
a jittery jade jackal juggling
a kinky khaki king knitting
a loony lime leprechaun lassoing
a monocled maroon madman marching
a nightmarish navy nastie nipping
an outrageous orange ogre oozing
a phoolish purple phantom phoning
a quadruple quicksilver quagga quaking
a revolting red rattlesnake rock 'n' rolling
a spotty scarlet spectre spitting
a terrible turquoise troll trampolining
an ugly umber uncle umpiring
a violent violet vampire vibrating
a whiskery white werewolf windsurfing
a yucky yellow yak yelling
a zitty zinc zombie zapping
inside
the
'Horrible
House'!

WES MAGEE

Illustrated by Gary Davies

As, As, As . . .

As slow as a start
as stopped as a heart
as thin as a chip
as chapped as a lip
as dour as a door
as high as the floor
as far as away
as near as today
as dreamy as far
as tall as a star
as dark as a lock
as stopped as a clock
as slow as a hiss
as near as a miss
as slim as an 'i'
as puzzled as 'y'
as warm as a purr
as boring as sir
as boring as sir
as boring as sir
as scrunched as a list
as white as a fist
as bold as a blizzard
as old as a wizard
as sad as the sea
as fit as a flea
as sick as our cat
as yukky as that
as slow as an end
as there as a friend
as quick as a kiss
as finished as this.

Robert Hull

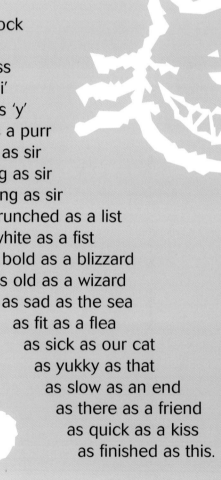

The Legend of the Lambton Worm

There's a very famous story
About a serpent and a well —
The story of the Lambton worm
A story I will tell

It happened one fine Monday
In the forest near a lake,
That the Lord of Lambton Castle
Came upon a snake.

It was a tiny wriggly thing
With a rather fishy smell,
So the Lord of Lambton Castle
Dropped it down a nearby well

Then he forgot about it
And went fighting far away,
But the worm grew and grew
To be slimy, fat and grey.

One day it slithered from the well
And roaring like a leopard,
It swallowed up a flock of sheep,
the sheepdog and the shepherd.

For years and years the creature lived
Devouring all it saw,
When one day brave Lord Lambton
Came back from the war.

He put his helmet on his head
And with his sword and shield,
He climbed up every mountain and
He looked in every field.

Until he found the Lambton Worm
With eyes of fiery red
And he lifted up his great sharp sword
And chopped off the big black head.

Then he cut it into pieces
And he dropped it down the well
And that was the end of the Lambton Worm
— So storytellers tell.

GERVASE PHINN

Illustrated by Kingsley Wiggin

Acknowledgements

Not Always a Perfect Place by Judy Waite, ©Judy Waite 1998

Raiders! by Lynne Benton from *Raiders!* published by Heinemann Educational (Literacy World series) 1998

A Jumble for the Queen by Julia Donaldson from *A Jumble for the Queen* published by Heinemann Educational (Literacy World Series) 1998

The Stove Haunting by Bel Mooney, from *The Stove Haunting*, ©Reed Books. Reproduced with permission of David Higham Associates on behalf of the author.

Family Photo Album by James Carter, ©James Carter 1998

My Grandpa by Ian Souter. First published in *You Just Can't Win - Poems of Family Life*, Blackie 1991, ©Ian Souter

Something Told the Wild Geese by Rachel Field, from *A Calendar of Poems*, Bell & Hyman, 1986, ©Rachel Field.

Snow Spell by Berlie Doherty from *Walking on Air*, HarperCollins 1993. Reproduced with permission of David Higham Associates on behalf of the author, ©Berlie Doherty

Time Spinner by Roy Apps, from *Time Spinner*, Andersen Press/Red Fox, reproduced with permission of Andersen Press, ©the author, Roy Apps

Metalmiss by Linda Pitt, from *Metalmiss*, Andersen Press/Red Fox, reproduced with permission of Andersen Press, ©the author, Linda Pitt

The Tide Rises, the Tide Falls by Henry Wadsworth Longfellow, out of copyright

Windy Nights by Robert Louis Stevenson, out of copyright

The Iron Man by Ted Hughes, from *The Iron Man*, Faber & Faber, reproduced with permission of Faber & Faber, ©Ted Hughes

The Invisible Beast by Jack Prelutsky, from *The Headless Horseman Hunts Tonight*, William Morrow, ©Jack Prelutsky

Before the Hunt by Lari Williams, from *You'll Love This Stuff*, Cambridge University Press, 1986

The Hobbit by J.R.R. Tolkein, from *The Hobbit* by J.R.R. Tolkein (HarperCollins). Reproduced with permission of HarperCollins Publishers.

Basia's Birthday Present by Robin Mellor, ©Robin Mellor reproduced by permission of the author

Diary of a Killer Cat by Anne Fine from *Diary of a Killer Cat* by Anne Fine, Hamish Hamilton Children's Books 1994, ©Anne Fine 1994, reproduced by permission of Penguin Books Ltd

Bill's New Frock by Anne Fine from *Bill's New Frock*, Methuen Children's Books. Reprinted with permission of Egmont Children's Books Ltd, ©Anne Fine

Cheat! by Judy Waite from *Cheat!* published by Heinemann Educational (Literacy World series) 1998

Hikers Haikus by Vernon Scannell, from *Travelling Light* The Bodley Head 1991, ©Vernon Scannell

Tomb Tunes by John Kitching, from *Parent-free Zone*, Macmillan, ©John Kitching reproduced by permission of the author

My Pet by Tony Bradman, reproduced by permission of The Agency (London) Ltd ©Tony Bradman 1993, first published by Blackie in *My First has Gone Bonkers*

A Who'z Who of the 'Horrible House' by Wes Magee ©the author, Wes Magee 1995

As, As, As... by Robert Hull, from *Stargazer*, Hodder & Stoughton 1997, reproduced with permission of Hodder & Stoughton

The Legend of the Lambton Worm by Gervase Phinn from *Touches of Beauty* Roselea Publications, 1995

Every effort has been made to trace copyright holders but we would be glad to rectify any omissions at the next reprint.